C000311351

TI

LANCASHIRE
(Lanky)
DIALECT

Compilation and Stories by Ernest Ford
Cartoons by Pete

© Coveropen Ltd. 1991

ISBN 1 873873 00 X

First Published June 1991 by
Coveropen Ltd,.
P.O. Box 60, Wigan WN1 2QB

Designed and produced by
Graphic Design Ltd., Wigan.

"I'm fain to be wick."

WELCOME to Lancashire; we are very pleased to see you. If you have decided to spend a little time amongst us friendly folk you will not be disappointed.

Quite apart from offering the finest and most varied landscape in the British Isles, you will hear some fascinating, rich and hypnotic sounds called *Lancashire dialect* or simply 'LANKY'.

It is often thought by our southern friends and sometimes even by our friends from a point more nothern than our own, that Lancashire consists solely of flat-capped inhabitants, with a 'Coronation Street' around every corner. These pockets of Lanca-shire can still be found if the visitor so insists and we make no effort to hide the fact. The old two-up-and-two-down terraced home is still a common feature of the region and though increasingly rare, some householders still read their news-papers whilst sitting in the 'closet' at the bottom of a stone-flagged yard. This is the Lancashire of old that refuses to give in.

"It's as plain as a pikestaff."

's all talk and sez wt."

Lancashire folk both rich and poor are well-known for 'working hard' and 'playing hard'. To enjoy the warmth and sincerity of 'born and bred' Lancashire folk and to listen to their dry humour is an experience never-to-be forgotten by any visitor to this north west corner of England. Naturally if you can understand and converse, so much the better. Remember its the easiest thing in the world to have a conversation with Lancashire folk it is extremely unlikely that you will ever be met with embarrassed silence.

If a 'native' should nod at you and say *"How do?"* or *"Art awe reet?"* Smile, for is is a Lancashire welcome which means "How are you?" or Are you alright?" It is a friendly ought from Lancashire folk who gularly enquire of one another's ell-being.

If you find in some cases the alect is beyond comprehension, en *Albert's Easy Teach Yourself ancashire Dialect* is a must for ou. Hopefully you will not only e educated but entertained by the ords that follow.

nyhow, enjoy your visit to Lanshire. Hopefully you will conder it a life enriching xperience.

"It's a poor bally, uz cawnt warm a cowd meyt and prayto pie."

3

HAVE YOU HEARD THESE WORDS?

A glossary of dialect words and phrases compiled to assist the visitor to Lancashire.

LANCASHIRE	MEANING
A	
Abeawt	About
Anyweer	Anywhere
Appen	Perhaps
Areawnd	Around
Awe'l	All
Awe'm	I'm
Awf	Off
Awlreet	Alright
Ax	Ask
Axed	Asked
Axin	Asking
B	
Babbi	Baby
Bally	Stomach
Beawnt	Going to
Beawt	Without
Bet'thur	Better
Beying	Buying
Bin	Been
Boowuth	Both

LANCASHIRE	MEANING
C	
Caw	Call
Cawed	Called
Cawnt	Cannot
Caws	Calls
Ceawncil	Council
Ceawnted	Counted
Clooas	Clothes
Coom	Come
Con	Can
Corrons	Currants
Cowd	Cold
Cruckt	Crooked
D	
Deawn	Down
Doower	Door
Dowter	Daughter
Dug	Dog
E	
Eawt	Out
Eawtside	Outside
Een	Eyes
Eyter	Eater
Eytin	Eating
Etten	Eaten

LANCASHIRE	MEANING
F	
Fain	Glad
Fall	Faw
Feesh	Fish
Floower	Floor
Fro	From
Fust	First
G	
Geet	Got
Gi	Give
Gooin	Going
Gowd	Gold
Gradely	Goodly
H	
Heaw	How
Heawf	Half
Heawr	Hour
Heawse	House
Heyt	Height
Hommer	Hammer
Honds	Hands
Howlder	Holder
I	
Imbook	Hymnbook
Inurt	Inward

LANCASHIRE	MEANING

J

Jawnt	Jaunt
Jerrt	Jerk
Jeyn	Join

K

Keyy	Key
Kilt	Killed

L

Larn	Learn
Leet	Light
Leet	Let
Leets	Lights
Leeust	Least
Let'thur	Letter
Lowse	Lose

M

Meawth	Mouth
Met	Might
Meyt	Meat
Mooest	Most
Mon	Man
Monny	Many
Mun	Must

LANCASHIRE	MEANING

N

Naer	Near
Neet	Night
Noan	None
Nowt	Nothing
Neaw	Now

O

Oer	Over
Onert	Honoured
Owd	Old
Owt	Anything

P

Papper	Paper
Peawnd	Pound
Peys	Peas
Prayto	Potatoe
Praytus	Potatoes

Q

Quare	Queer
Querthur	Quarter

R

Rappit	Rabbit
Reawnd	Round
Reet	Right

LANCASHIRE	MEANING
Reych	Reach

S

Scoo	School
Sell	Self
Set'day	Saturday
Sez	Says
Skrike	Cry
Summat	Something
Speyk	Speak
Stond	Stand

T

T'	The
Tae	Tea
Tan	Taken
Tawk	Talk
Tek	Take
Tha	You
Theer	There
Thee	You
Towd	Told
Thi	You

U

Um	Them
Umteen	Plenty
Un	And
Untee	Untie
Ut	At

LANCASHIRE	MEANING
Uv	Of
Uz	Us/As/We

V

Vawse	Vase

W

Waggin	Wagon
Wannt	Want
Wark	Work
Watter	Water
Weer	Where
Weesh	Wish
Wesh	Wash
Wi	With
Wick	Week/Alive
Wilt	Will you
Wom	Home
Wor	What

Y

Yed	Head
Yedwarch	Headache
Yer	Listen
Yerd	Heard
Yerhole	Earhole
Yo	You
Yon	Yonder

"By gum — when I were a lad we 'ad to mek 'em oursell".

11

HOW ABOUT THESE DOUBLE WORDS?

I ASSUME that you got through the single words alright and to prove to you that Lancashire dialect isn't as silly as some might think, here are a few examples where one word of dialect means two of Standard English.

If the visitor could speak Lancashire dialect he could say twice as much with half the effort. Anyhow, keep your ears open for two words condensed to one *Lanky* word.

Art	Are you
Azer	Has she
Bowtum	Bought them
Connit	Can it
Diddy	Did he
Erdid	She did
Ferus	For us
Guduz	Good as
Howdim	Hold him
Itwer	It was
Lerim	Let him
Musta	Must I
Nethen	Now then
Owdo	How do
Purrit	Put it
Sesit	Says it
Thend	The end
Unawl	And all
Wilta	Will you
Yawl	You all

"Get a door on that cabin, Albert....you just don't look respectable".

THESE PHRASES ARE EVEN BETTER

NOW that you are progressing in the speech of the north countryman it is time to let you tackle the 'phrase', the ones you are bound to hear in shops, pubs or clubs.

If you feel that you have mastered the *Lanky Tawk* then try out some of these phrases on your friends. If you are met with blank stares, *tha'l afta try harder!*

Oozer theesclugs?	Whose are these clogs?
Wossupwithi?	Whats the matter with you
Berritdunt wark	I bet that it doesn't work
Frozzent deeuth	Frozen to death
Snotworitwer	Its not what it was
Howdonabit owdlad	Hold on a bit old lad
Diddy gerritwom?	Did he get it home?
Ayowta browtim	I ought to have brought him
Ifitsthine sesso	If its yours say so
Cloditint bin	Throw it in the bin
Izyomaggie cumin?	Is your Maggie coming?
Snorawfreet	Its not half right
Azierd izsel?	Has he heard himself
Ast binmenbin?	Has the binmen been?
Cozitint thine	Because it isn't yours
Aziadiz hurcut?	Has he had his hair cut?
Dustmeent dustmon?	Do you mean the dustman?
Duzit stopeer?	Does it stop here?
Iyaz izleeter	I have his lighter
Erzbrokken erwerd	She's broken her word
Eemunt cumineer	He mustn't come in here
Eeaziz ownroad	He has his own way
Erazir fawts	She has her faults
Lerrer gowilta	Let her go will you
Snorawlusreet	Its not always right

14

"Albert, you're a man of the world...."

OER THEER

SAM Smalley and his wife had just been transported by holiday flight from Lancashire to Hollywood thanks to winning a competition held by his local travel agent.

Excited at wanting to see everything about the place he left his wife to unpack whilst he trod light-heartedly along one avenue after another until he finally discovered that he was lost.

"Owd mon. I weesh uz I'd waited 'til t' morn for t'suss place eawt", he said to himself. Further along the road he noticed a handyman mending dry stone wall. "Hey thee", he shouted, before realising that the American wouldn't know what the word 'thee' meant. "Er, excuse me", he offered in his telephone English. The man turned around and gave a laugh as he began to speak. "Its awe'l reet owd lad. Tha's no need fer t'put thi 'airs un graces' on fer me".

The Lancashire accent coming from the American's mouth took Sam by surprise. "Tha con tawk proper afther all", Sam said laughingly and threw his cap into the air. "I owt do", said the handyman. "I coom fro Wigin only two 'ear sin. Un wear has tha cum fro?"

"Leigh, bet'thur known as Leyth!"

"Tha knows, im uz I wark for is a millionaire un he originated fro Bowton", explained the handyman. "He's wot they caw eccentric. He keeps mon-eytin crocodiles in his pool".

Continued on page 18

16

"I've got a bottle of whisky for my wife".
"What a gradely swop".

"Gi oer", said Sam. "Hey up. I think us he's cummin oer 'ere". "Hello", said the millionaire. "Are you a sightseer?" Sam answered in his Lancashire accent and was immediately offered hospitality by the millionaire.

"I'm having a party", the millionaire said, "will you join us?"

Sam looked across an expanse of lawn larger than a golf course and noticed a crowd standing around the swimming pool. As the guest of honour, Sam was forced to the front to stand next to the millionaire, who then, in sight of everyone, operated a lever to allow a massive crocodile into the pool.

"Listen everyone", the millionaire said. "I'll give anything anyone wants who is brave enough to enter the pool with the crocodile". A cry of excitement then went up. Quick as a flash Sam was in the water thrashing his way across the pool, with the crocodile in hot pursuit. The water seemed to be almost on fire as the brave Lancastrian zoomed to the other side. With panache, he jumped safely onto land just before the jaws of the beast could snap shut.

The millionaire rushed over wringing his hands with pride that a little Lancastrian man should be the one to show such bravery. "Well done, well done", he patted the back of a dripping Sam. "I will keep my promise. You can have anything you want. What is it, a car, yacht or an aeroplane?"

Continued on page 20

"Don't go so far out Ethel".
"Why not, mummy is out a
long way".
That's different, thi mother's
insured".

"Nowt o them", Sam answered, looking uneasy in his wet suit "But I'll tell thi wot I do wannt". "I want name o that bugger uz pushed me in!"

FARM WARK

YOUNG Alfie was forever turning up late for school. The lad was the son of a farmer and obviously farm jobs were shared between the family. The teacher made allowances for Alfie's indiscretions; that was until one particular morning, when Alfie slipped into the classroom a full one hour late.

"Now then, now then", shouted Miss Barstow in the most threatening voice she could muster. "I'm reet sorry miss", answered a nervous Alfie now beginning to shake, "but I had mi farm duties for t'see to miss". "And I suppose farm duties are more important than school?" Miss Barstow said as she closed in on the crouching Alfie. "And what may I ask did this duty entail?" "I had for t' tek the bull deawn to the cow miss", explained Alfie. "And..." Miss Barstow slammed her ruler onto the desk. "Couldn't your father do that?" "No miss", explained Alfie. "It has to be the bull!"

CEAWNTIN UP

GERAWF mi". The unkempt lady protested to the official before propelling herself to a seat besides Nell, as she awaited her turn to be called before the magistrates. "I cawnt stond men wi warm honds", she protested again. "Is that reet?" Nell moved a little further

Haircut!
Yes sir!
Which one, sir?

along the bench to avoid the alcohol fumes coming from the toothless mouth of the newcomer.

"Tha doesn't need for t' move eawt mi road", she snapped. "I'm not nasty tha knows".

"No, its just the..." Nell wafted her hand about and the newcomer immediately saw the point and laughed.

"Oh, its that", she said. "Ive just bin on a whisky diet". "I reetly cawnt say us I've ever yerd o that whisky diet...", Nell said. "Un wot did yo lowse?" "Abeawt four days!" The woman said followed by a loud cackle.

A police constable then passed by and gave the two women a surly look. "Look at im", she shouted after him. "Beawt uz they'd awe'l bi eawt o wark — snotty nosed lot!"

Nell tried to quieten her down before she brought further trouble upon them. The woman then said: "They hev their favourites tha knows, un I can prove it". "Heaw does t'make that eawt?" Nell wanted to know.

The woman then twisted her neck round as if making sure that nobody was within earshot. "Listen", she said in a low voice. "Once when I were tan in for being drunk, there wuz a doctor stondin theer on t' same charge. Well, they ax thi for t' read summat off a card, un 'e went fust".

"Un what were it ?" Nell's curiosity now aroused.

"They gid im a card uz read, 'the cow jumped over the moon', but not me. Mine read 'Cissie saw six thick thistle sticks', un doest know sommut? Noan uv um in t' cop shop could get their meawths reawnd that".

"Owd mon!" said Nell. "That's not reet. Have yo bin here afore?" Nell continued.

Neaw Fred, if tha not comin' out con
I 'ave thi ale?

"Oh aye, monny a time, I'm a 'season ticket' howder. She then looked at Nell and said: "Un wor are yo here fer?" Before Nell could reply, her name was being called and she was escorted into another room to face the judge.

"And what have we here then?" The judge looked sternly at Nell. "A fust charge one eh?"

"Shoplifting your honour", shouted the clerk.

"And what did she take", the judge asked.

"A tin of tomatoes sir!"

"Right", said the judge. "And is the tin available?" The tin which Nell was caught stealing was then produced. The judge then instructed a clerk to open it.

"Now then", said the judge to Nell, "how many tomatoes are there in the tin?"

Nell prodded away inside the tin until each tomato was counted. "There are six tomatoes here sir".

"Right", he replied. "Six tomatoes, then that is what you will get. Six months. One for each tomato!"

Nell buckled at the knees and turned deathly pale. "I'll tell yo summat owd lad..." she said to the judge. "I'm gradely fain uz I put yon tin o baked beans back!!"

GOLF CLUBBED

THE Golf Club lounge was quite impressive with its oak panelled walls and its decorative plaster ceiling. "Tha con bet uz tha couldn't afford to build owt like this neawadays", George Oldfield said to himself as he moved along the wall of photographs which displayed past and present members of the club. "With onny luck my mug-

"Oh thank you so much for finding my little darling....where was he".

"A chap 'ad 'im on a pole weshin' a window wi' 'im.

shot could be 'angin' theer". He said to himself as he touched a spot on the wall. Just then a cough from behind him made him swivel quickly.

"Mr. Oldfield?", said an over-sized person emerging from an oak door. "Er, aye. That's me", George replied. "I'm the Secretary. We geet thi let'thur last wick axin if tha could jeyn uz", went on the Secretary. "Oh", said George, unable to think of anything else. "Aye", he went on, "un thats why wiv sent fer thi to come fer this interview. Wilt follow me!" The two men entered into a palatial room where another over-sized man sat upright in his golf attire. "This eer mon is our President.

Sit thi deawn", said the Secretary.

"Now then", the President mumbled. "I see you have asked to be a member. Do you know anthing about golf?" George was asked. "Aye, I know summat abeawt golf awe'l reet", went on George. "Un mooest of t' big names uz play it". "Oh?" blurted out the officials in unison. "Lee Travino caws ut our heawse when he's playin areawnd here un Tony Jacklin rings me up neaw un then. Then there's...."

"Enough, enough", cut in the President. "You know that you'll have to step outside whilst we decide". "Thats reet enough, said Joe, "but con yo be quick abeawt it because I wannt ter catch a bus from 'ere at ten past eight".

The two officials quickly confided in each other. "He's the biggest liar I have ever come across", said the President trying to stifle a laugh. "Not heawf", said a bemused Secretary. "There's no bus from here at ten past eight!"

"Your toothbrush?
Oh, don't worry owd pal,
I thought it belonged
to th' hotel".

MIXED VEG

FRED Duckworth relished the hot summer sun upon his back as he walked robot-style from his home in Leigh to seek out his old workmate Bill Green, whom he knew lived in a particular area of Bolton. Although his military training had prepared him for such a trek, he was glad to see the traffic lights at Four Lane Ends.   Proceeding on his way it wasn't long before Bolton's outskirts came into view. He made his way through the side streets to an area which he thought might be the one he was looking for. Then he spotted an old lady stoning' her flags, a once-regular Lancashire household chore that Joe thought he might never see again.

"Excuse me luv", Joe said as he approached her. "Could yo tell mi weer I con find th' Cobble Street?"

The old woman stood up: "Cobble Street? Awe th' streets are cobbled areawned here". She wiped her nose with the back of her hand. "Oh aye! I know weer it is neaw. Con yo see yon third row? Try theer".

Sure enough the old lady was right. Cobble Street came into view. Joe then pulled a piece of paper from his pocket, noticed the number. He knocked on the door of the third house in the row and waited. A woman answered.

"Excuse me", said Joe, "could I speyk to Bill". The woman went white then fell to the floor in a faint. Bill's son came hurriedly to the door. "I'm sorry abeawt this", he apologised. "Yo see, mi dad's just deed".

"Before I die, Albert,
I want to make a
confession....
I've been unfaithful".
"I know, owd lass,
that's why
I've poisoned thee".

Joe immediately offered his condolences, "I'm reet sorry", "heaw did it happen?"

"Well yo see", said the lad. "We awlus have a cabbage fer Setday dinner off mi dad's allotment. He were bending oer to cut this cabbage, when he collapsed".

"Oh dear", said Joe. "Un wot did yo do?"

"We oppened a tin o peys". The lad told an astonished Joe.

TRAVELLIN' LEET

THE light aircraft swayed to and fro above the clouds as the pilot struggled to keep control if his 'bird in the sky'. From the look on his face it was easy to see that his struggle was coming to an end. The engine spluttered, coughed, then stopped. "Owd mon, owd mon", gasped the pilot as he tried every knob and switch in sight.

It was obvious that the aircraft would have to be evacuated and he moved inside to inform the three passengers. As well as himself there was a bishop, a professor who they called 'brains', and a boy scout.

"I suppose uz I don't have fer t' tell yo lot uz we have t' tek our hook eawt of here reet neaw". Without much discussion they all nodded in agreement.

The saddest blow of all came when the pilot informed them that although there were four people on board, there was in fact only three parachutes. Before anyone could complain the pilot grabbed a parachute and an inflatable dinghy and jumped. 'Brains' hurried grabbed another chute because he believed that the world would need him and his knowledge. This left the bishop and the boy scout behind.

The bishop turned to the scout and decided to put his faith in the Lord by and offered him the last parachute. "Here", he said, "thee tek it".

Praising the bishop for his unselfish decision, the scout told him that there was not real difficulty at all because there were in fact two parachutes left and not just one.

"Yo see", the scout told the amazed bishop. "Yon mon uz we cawed 'Brains' jumped eawt wearing mi haversack!"

Congratulations - by now you should not only be educated in the art of speaking in the *Lancashire dialect* but hopefully, you have also been entertained.

If this little book has helped to make your visit to the region more enjoyable then the effort has been worthwhile ... Meanwhile from the people of Lancashire ...

Wish thi weel 'til we sithee agen.

LANCASHIRE ALPHABET

A. is for AWLUS the friendship thats here
B. is for BET'THUR you wont find it I fear
C. is for CRUCKT but not Blackpool Tower
D. is for DOWTER as fair as a flower
E. is for EYTIN such paces abound
F. is for FEESH in most cafes is found
G. is for GOWD which glints in the sun
H. is for HEAWSE in the 'public' there's fun
I. is for IMBOOK but there's time yet for that
J. is for JAWNT and a 'kiss me quick' hat
K. is for KEYY which will open your door
L. is for LEET and will let you see more
M. is for MUNNY in your pocket or purse
N. is for NOWT if you've got it feel worse
O. is for OWT which is better than nothing
P. is for PEAWND and your lips start a frothing
Q. is for QUARE I'm glad that's out my mind
R. is for REET that's how most people you'll find
S. is for SPEYK and I'm teaching you that
T. is for TAE I could sup out of my hat
U. is for UMTEEN that's times without number
V. is for VAWSE which holds flowers, sometimes lumber
W. is for WATTER that everyone needs
X. is on coupon that gamblers all plead
Y. is for YED we keep clear and keep light
Z. is the noise that we make every night.